Life of Fred ®
Going Home

Stanley F. Schmidt, Ph.D.

Polka Dot Publishing

ISBN: 978-1-937032-41-8
Printed and bound in the United States of America
Polka Dot Publishing   Reno, Nevada

To order books in the Life of Fred series,

visit our website PolkaDotPublishing.com

Questions or comments? Email the author at lifeoffred@yahoo.com

First Printing
This book was illustrated by the author with additional clip art furnished under license from Nova
Development Corporation, which holds the copyright to that art.

Dear Parent,
    Fred and Kingie will have many wonderful memories of their trip.
    In this book we . . .
≫ review the days of the week
≫ show how not to sell a house
≫ introduce the ordinal numbers: first, second, third
≫ give a picture of what 100 looks like.

    In these 18 books the reading level has inched up slowly. The vocabulary has become larger, and the sentences have become less simple.
    Ahead lies ten Elementary Series and three Intermediate Series books (each 128 pages). Then at the middle school level are three pre-algebra books which also have physics, biology, and economics stirred in. At the high school level are the traditional four math courses: beginning algebra, advanced algebra, geometry, and trig. And a high school chemistry course. And four language arts books. At the college level: two years of calculus, a year of statistics and upper-division linear algebra. By that time, your child may be reading these Eden Series books to his/her kids!

With much love,
Stan

Chapter One

Sunday

Monday

Tuesday

Wednesday

Thursday

Today ⋙⁺ Friday

Saturday

The next bus will come on Friday.

Fred and Kingie go home today.

Kingie packed his hats.

King of French Fries

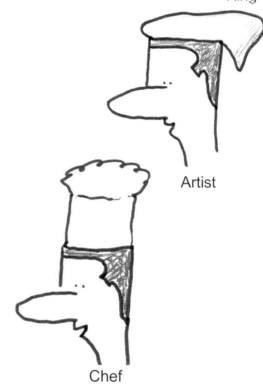

Artist

Chef

Tree Planter

Then he packed the rest of his stuff.

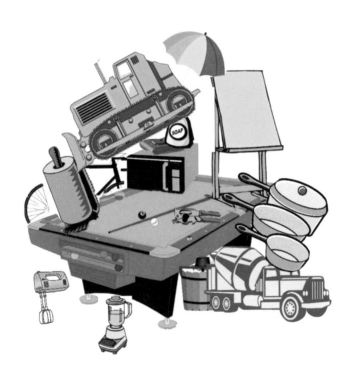

Fred made a sign and put it on his house.

The sign was hard to read.

Fred put the sign near the bottom of the house because he was only three feet tall.

Here is what the sign said.

No one saw the sign except the ducks.

And ducks can't read.

One of the ducks ate the sign.

Fred walked among his fruit trees.

He was looking for more fruit.

There wasn't any.

He didn't notice that his sign was gone.

Chapter Two

They turned the lights off.

They took their stuff to the bus stop.

They waited for the bus.

The bus came.

This bus was dark red.

Fred and Kingie got on the bus.

The bus was going to KITTENS.

These are kittens.

The bus was not going to kittens.

The bus was going to KITTENS University.

1. KITTENS University is in Kansas.
2. Fred and Kingie live in the Math Building at KITTENS.

KITTENS is an acronym for Kansas Institute for Teaching Technology, Engineering and the Natural Sciences.

map of Kansas

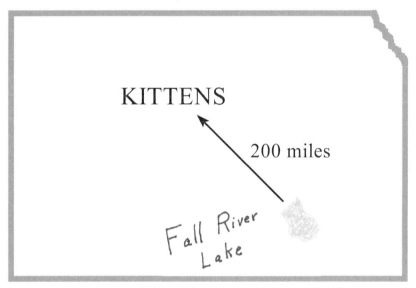

They looked at the map.

They had 200 miles to go before they got to their home.

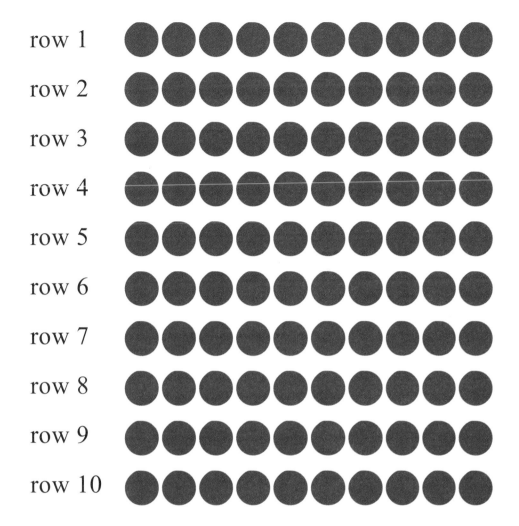

row 1
row 2
row 3
row 4
row 5
row 6
row 7
row 8
row 9
row 10

Fred make 100 dots on a piece of paper.

Each dot was the color of the bus.

There were ten rows.

In math, rows are horizontal ↔
and columns are vertical ↕.

He drew another 100 dots.

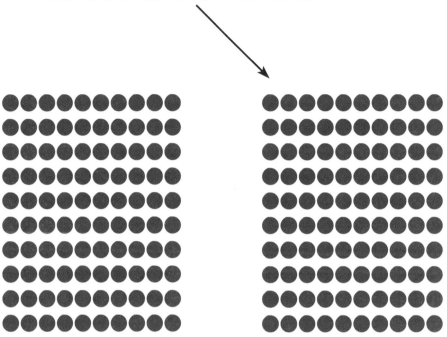

He drew 200 dots.

It was 200 miles to home.

$$\begin{array}{r} 100 \\ +\ 100 \\ \hline 200 \end{array}$$

Kingie looked out the bus window. He was looking for something to paint. He took some photos.

"Elephants" photo by Kingie

"Metal Man" photo by Kingie

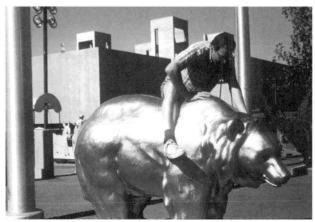
"Young Man on Bear" photo by Kingie

Kingie got out his brushes and oil
paints.

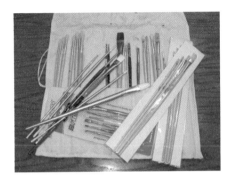

He told Fred, "When you take a photo,
you get a picture of a young man on a bear,

"Young Man on Bear"
photo by Kingie

but when you do oil painting, you can make
any changes that you like."

Kingie painted. He made some changes from the photo.

"Duck on Bear"
by Kingie

Fred looked out the window and saw a sign.

Fred made 50 dots on a piece of paper.

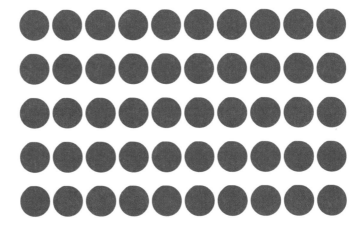

A couple on the bus saw Kingie's painting. They loved it.

"Duck on Bear"
by Kingie

We'll give you $5,000 for that painting.

Fred asked, "Would you like to buy my dots. I have 50 of them."

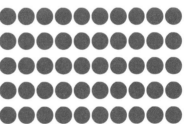

They said, "No thank you."

When the bus was 20 miles from
KITTENS, Fred drew 20 blue dots.

When it was one mile from Fred's
home, he drew one big red dot.

The bus arrived at KITTENS
University.

Fred and Kingie got off the bus.

Kingie left all his stuff
with the man at the bus stop.
Kingie would pick it up later.

They walked to the university.

entrance to KITTENS

They walked through the gardens.

They looked
at the water fountain.

They came to the Math Building. This is where Fred and Kingie live.

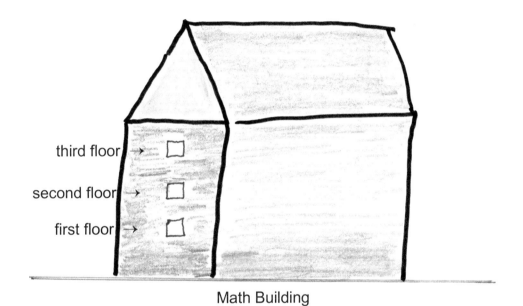

third floor →

second floor →

first floor →

Math Building

They live in room 314 on the third floor.

They ran up the stairs
from the first floor to the second
and from the second floor
to the third.

They ran down the hallway to their
home in room 314.

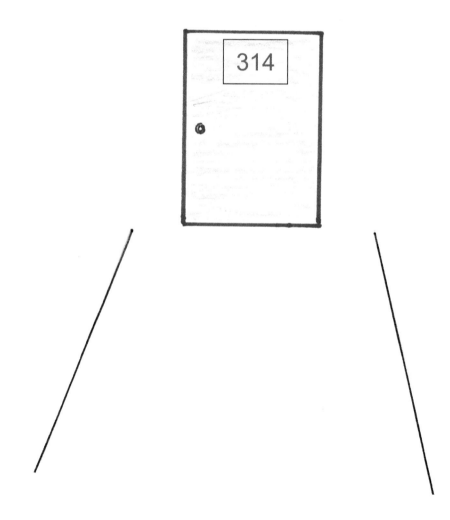

They were so happy to be home again.

Fred gave his doll a big hug.

Fred looked out the window from his room on the third floor.

He wondered whether he could see Fall River Lake.

He couldn't. It was too far away.